Walter Hood Fitch
A Celebration

ROYAL BOTANIC GARDENS, KEW

Walter Hood Fitch
A Celebration

JAN LEWIS

LONDON: HMSO

ISBN 0 11 250066 8

FRONTISPIECE
Magnolia campbellii (from Joseph Dalton Hooker's
Illustrations of Himalayan Plants)

 HMSO

HMSO publications are available from:

HMSO Publications Centre
(Mail and telephone orders only)
PO Box 276, London, SW8 5DT
Telephone orders 071-873 9090
General enquiries 071-873 0011
(queuing system in operation for both numbers)

HMSO Bookshops
49 High Holborn, London, WC1V 6HB 071-873 0011 (counter service only)
258 Broad Street, Birmingham, B1 2HE 021-643 3740
Southey House, 33 Wine Street, Bristol, BS1 2BQ 0272-264306
9–21 Princess Street, Manchester, M60 8AS 061-834 7201
80 Chichester Street, Belfast, BT1 4JY 0232-238451
71 Lothian Road, Edinburgh, EH3 9AZ 031-228 4181

HMSO's Accredited Agents
(see Yellow Pages)

and through good booksellers

Printed in the United Kingdom for HMSO
Dd 291788 C50 12/91

Contents

Foreword

*T*HIS BOOK COMMEMORATES THE CENTENARY OF THE
death of an outstanding botanical artist of the Victorian era. Walter Hood
Fitch was never officially on the staff of the Royal Botanic Gardens, Kew;
however, as artist for *Curtis's Botanical Magazine*, he drew many of the new and
spectacular plants at Kew for some forty years and also illustrated books by
Kew staff.

When Fitch was an apprentice pattern drawer in a calico mill in Glasgow,
his potential artistic talent was brought to the attention of William (later Sir
William) Hooker, Professor of Botany at Glasgow University. Fitch was
persuaded to abandon textile design for employment with Hooker, mounting
specimens and illustrating botanical lectures while at the same time acquiring
a knowledge of botany and developing his aptitude for flower painting.

When Hooker left Glasgow to become Director of Kew, Fitch came with
him, leaving his employ in 1860 only when he was fully confident of his
ability to attract commissions. He illustrated botanical monographs and
textbooks and contributed to horticultural magazines. The clarity of his
line-drawings for George Bentham's *Handbook of the British Flora* (1865)
ensured the book's popularity for many years. He drew cryptograms with the
same unerring touch that distinguishes his rendering of flowering plants.
Flamboyant and exotic flowers such as rhododendrons, orchids and the giant
royal water-lily, *Victoria amazonica*, had an ideal interpreter in Fitch, who
always painted with impressive panache.

His extraordinary visual memory and sound botanical knowledge enabled
Fitch to capture the essential qualities of a flower. He had the ability, rare
amongst botanical artists, to compose accurate portraits based on a
combination of dried specimens and often meagre field sketches. He was also a
consummate lithographer who could execute his bold fluent lines straight on
to the lithographic stone.

His name is commemorated in the genus *Fitchia* but a more appropriate
memorial is the corpus of drawings he has left us to admire and enjoy. A token
selection has been made for this book from those now held in the Kew Library.
We are fortunate to have Jan Lewis, a descendant of Fitch and herself an artist,
to write this tribute to a remarkable man.

GHILLEAN T PRANCE
Director
Royal Botanic Gardens, Kew

Acknowledgements

I WOULD LIKE TO THANK THE FOLLOWING PEOPLE, WITHOUT whose help this book would not have been possible: my husband John, for his constant support, encouragement and practical help in the last year of research, particularly with genealogy and in the additions to the list of Fitch works. Grace Woodbridge, who kindly let me stay in her home and gave me free access to all the notes made by her friend Mea Allan for her book *The Hookers of Kew*. The leads gained from this reading proved to be most valuable. Gavin Bridson and the late Wilfrid Blunt, who helped guide my steps in the initial stages of research in 1981. Desmond Meikle, botanist, who helped enormously on several occasions with his personal recollections of the Fitch family at Kew, and whose particular interest in Fitch encouraged me to continue.

I am grateful to the following institutions for the use of their facilities: the Linnean Society of London, the Lindley Library, the Royal Horticultural Society and the British Museum (Natural History).

I would like to say a special thank you to the many descendants of the Hooker family who have fed and entertained me in their homes, and given me access to their treasures, and to the few remaining descendants of the Fitch family.

My thanks are also due to the Director of the Royal Botanic Gardens, Kew for allowing me to use the Herbarium, Library and Archives; Professor Lucas; Sylvia Fitzgerald and Marilyn Ward; Professor W T Stearn; Ray Desmond and Valerie Walley.

Finally, my grateful thanks to the Marc Fitch Fund (no relative), for the award of a research grant in 1984.

Introduction

WALTER HOOD FITCH WAS ONE OF THE MOST PROLIFIC botanical artists the world has ever known. Over 12,000 of his botanical drawings were published, and once his exploratory work, sketches, and an enormous amount of unpublished and non-botanical work have been taken into account, it is clear that he drew at speed, constantly and ceaselessly, every day of his life. His flamboyant but accurate drawings gained him international fame and recognition and provided vitally important records of an immense number of plants new to botany.

Botany was a way of life for him. In spite of his initial training as a landscape artist, he developed such a passion for plants that he spent his limited spare time botanising with friends for pleasure. His almost superhuman capacity for work and the speed with which he produced it were matched by great attention to botanical accuracy and tremendous versatility. He was equally at home working directly from nature, from dried plants, from the rough sketches of other artists, from verbal or written descriptions, or even from his own strong visual memory, and had an amazing ability to reconstruct his information, sometimes creating one plant from several specimens, or one landscape from several sketches. The fact that he worked as his own lithographer ensured that his work lost none of its vitality in the process of printing. He was the first draughtsman to produce really satisfactory drawings from dried herbarium specimens, and his abilities in this have never been bettered.

Fitch's prints are now collectors' items, valued as much for their beauty as for their scientific interest. His early experience in the cotton industry had exposed him to the prevailing fashions for French, Chinese and Indian designs, and these influences never left him. Oriental techniques usually emphasise the decorative quality of plants, whilst the European artist strives to portray the structure. Fitch's art was therefore a perfect combination of East and West.

His ability to compose lively designs that would fit into the restrictive area of a book's page was also acquired in those early days. He excelled at composition, and it is his arrangement of plants upon the page that so often distinguishes his art from that of others. A careful study of Fitch's better drawings will reveal a dissection specifically placed to lead the eye into the picture, and the clever turn of a leaf or stem to bring the eye back to the starting point. Once discovered, it will be seen that Fitch uses this device so often that it is obviously intentional. As Ehret had done, Fitch often relied upon the device of crossed diagonals, although he usually allowed the shape and individuality of each plant to dictate its own design.

Botanically, Fitch's work was not generally as meticulous as that of Ehret, Redouté or the Bauers, but he was able to grasp the character of a plant and express it with boldness and vigour in a style that has become known as 'Fitchian', breathing life into a plant drawing that would otherwise have become a stiff and scientific representation.

Fitch's later years were darkened by disagreements with one of his patrons, Sir Joseph Hooker, and a conviction that he had given his all to botany for a pittance and yet was unappreciated. Fitch's long relationship with the Hookers, as described briefly in the following chapters, was, in the main, one of mutual esteem and of great benefit to botany. While Fitch received a certain amount of reflected glory from his patrons, his illustrations helped them reach a wider public and thus enhance their own reputations as botanical scientists.

The work of Fitch and the Hookers is inseparable from the activities of the Royal Botanic Gardens at Kew. When the Gardens passed into public ownership and Sir William Hooker took over as the first Director in 1841, Fitch became Kew's unofficial artist, and he illustrated almost every book issued from there over the next forty years. He was not paid by the State, and yet he 'gave' nearly 3000 watercolour drawings to the Herbarium and Library, and continued to donate sets of lithographs to Kew long after he had retired. As Sir Joseph said in a letter to Disraeli: 'In Fitch's case, the Government has reaped where it has not sown.'

Those 'Kew' drawings were a constant source of irritation to Fitch, and yet if the Hookers had not insisted on their being given to Kew, not only would modern botany have been the poorer, but Fitch's name would not be held in such high esteem today. If Fitch had kept the drawings, as he so dearly wished, they would now be dispersed across Europe and the United States, for such has been the fate of his other work.

In 1892, at the time of his death, his reputation and fame were far-reaching, and countless appreciative obituary notices appeared in journals all over Europe. It was said of him that 'the quality of his work is such to preserve his name to posterity so long as botany and horticulture may continue to flourish.'

In 1992 the Royal Botanic Gardens at Kew, through its collection of Fitch drawings and its work in the international arena of botany and horticulture, continues to fulfil this prediction.

ONE

1817–1841
The Training of a Botanical Artist

WALTER HOOD FITCH WAS BORN IN GLASGOW ON 29 January 1817, the second son of John and Catherine Fitch. John Fitch was employed in the cloth trade, and by 1822 the family had moved to Leeds, a thriving centre for the industry. Walter joined his elder brother Alexander at Leeds Grammar School in 1827, where he studied Latin, Greek and mathematics.

Two years later, the family were back in Glasgow; eleven-year-old Walter was showing an increasing talent in drawing, and so became an assistant palette washer to Andrew Donaldson (1790–1846), one of Scotland's finest topographical artists. His was the earliest known artistic influence on Walter Fitch, and he instilled in that young mind a permanent love for landscape painting. After six months with Donaldson, Walter moved on to learn the art of lithography, probably in Glasgow's Trongate with Hugh Wilson, whose firm was responsible for the first chalk printing in Glasgow – a technique at which young Fitch became adept.

Walter Hood Fitch as a young man
Reproduced with kind permission of the British Museum (Natural History)

William Jackson Hooker

In January 1830, he became an apprentice pattern drawer in a mill owned by Henry Monteith, where he learnt to draw the Chinese and Indian patterns that were fashionable at the time. The swirls and shapes of these designs, and the way they fitted neatly on to the small printing blocks were to be a strong influence on his style as a botanical artist. Fitch showed much promise, and even in those days, when child labour was common, must have displayed a precocious talent to have been employed in the drawing office at such an early age.

Henry Monteith was a good friend of William Jackson Hooker, Regius Professor of Botany at Glasgow University, who since 1826 had been editor of *Curtis's Botanical Magazine*. This famous periodical, with which Fitch was to be associated for most of his life, was founded in 1787 by William Curtis as an illustrated record of new plants introduced from abroad to British gardens. (Also known as the *Botanical Magazine*, it was to survive until 1984, when it was succeeded by the *Kew Magazine*.)

Professor Hooker was an accomplished botanical artist, and was not only the magazine's editor but also its sole illustrator. By the time Fitch was working for Monteith, however, Hooker had decided that he needed help with the drawing of plants. Monteith had noticed his young pattern drawer's talent and, at his suggestion, Hooker decided to give Walter Fitch a trial.

Initially, Fitch spent his free evenings at Hooker's home, mounting dried specimens of plants under the professor's guidance. This he did so efficiently that Hooker lent him some books containing outline botanical prints. Walter copied these easily, and Hooker, impressed with the boy's talents, bought him out of his apprenticeship. By March 1834 Walter Fitch had started drawing and gluing down plants for Hooker, initially for 10 shillings a week. He spent his leisure hours reading books on botany, and was quick to learn the techniques of botanical drawing, morphology, anatomy and dissection.

Fitch was soon assisting Hooker in preparing a set of large-scale folio drawings of palms for his botanical lectures at the university. Fitch attended these, alongside the professor's own two sons William and Joseph, who were both studying medicine there. He got on well with Hooker's family – especially with Joseph Hooker, who was almost exactly his own age.

In just a few months, Walter Fitch became indispensable to William Hooker; he was reliable, and his drawing was fast and accurate. In turn, the young man offered Hooker his loyalty and respect. Hooker was now so confident of Fitch's ability that he entrusted him with the responsibility of drawing for *Curtis's Botanical Magazine*, and a few months later, on 1 October 1834, 'Walt' Fitch's first plate was published: pl.3353, *Mimulus lewisii*. Eight plates in this volume were drawn by Fitch, and after this he became virtually the sole artist for the magazine, his drawings being engraved on copper by Joseph Swan, a local printer.

By 1835, Fitch had drawn forty-two plates for volume 63 of the *Botanical Magazine* and fifteen plates for its *Companion*. He spent many hours on lecture drawings, and was now preparing 'A series of above 1,000 figures selected from the best sources to explain the terms employed in a course of lectures in Botany' for Hooker's *Botanical Illustrations*, published in 1837.

Hooker was knighted for his services to botanical science in April 1836, and soon began a new periodical – *Icones Plantarum* – with descriptions and illustrations of new or rare plants from his herbarium. The uncoloured plates were to be Fitch's total responsibility, making use of his ability to reconstitute dried herbarium specimens and produce drawings of them that appeared to be of living plants. The published plates were produced by lithography, an illustration process that gave Fitch a totally new sense of artistic freedom, as now no printer was required to engrave from his drawings.

These clear and simple illustrations were of a different character from those he had produced of living plants for the *Botanical Magazine*, and the flair for bold design that was to mark Fitch's style – particularly in the way the plants were positioned on the page – was already apparent. According to the Keeper of the Kew Herbarium, W Botting Hemsley, 'Under so able an instructor as Sir William Hooker, Fitch soon became proficient and even his early work reveals the artistic power of a genius.'

Sir William's reputation as one of the foremost botanists in Britain was rising rapidly, but he was so overworked that he was unable to complete the illustrations for two of his books. Fitch stepped in and completed ten quarto plates for *The Botany of Captain Beechey's Voyage* (1830–41), and a further twenty for *Flora Boreali-Americana* (1829–40); he also drew twenty-six plates for Hooker's *Botanical Illustrations*, 149 for the *Icones Plantarum*, and eighty-two for the *Botanical Magazine*. The prodigious Fitch, now twenty years old, was fully earning his current wage of 20 shillings a week.

Sir William now began work on *Genera Filicum* (1838–42), the first of his three great works on ferns, and Francis Bauer, the artist who had worked at Kew under the patronage of Sir Joseph Banks, offered forty drawings to start the series. Bauer's work was extremely delicate, and his analyses were painstaking pencil drawings washed over with colour. After some technical problems had been overcome, Fitch produced lithographs of Bauer's drawings, Joseph Hooker commenting 'To truthful delineation and colouring, perspective of every organ of a plant, and power of seizing the salient characteristics of habit etc, Fitch added a marvellous rapidity in execution'. Bauer was now old and ill, so Fitch drew and lithographed the rest of the eighty plates in this beautiful book, using soft chalk shading and minimal outline in a successful continuation of Bauer's style.

William Hooker's son Joseph had now qualified as a doctor, and in 1839 joined a British naval expedition as an assistant surgeon – a post that would also give him an opportunity for natural history research. The two ships, HMS *Erebus* and HMS *Terror*, left England in September on the greatest Antarctic expedition of the 19th century: 'For the Discovery and Attainment of the South Magnetic Pole'.

The following year saw the birth on October 24 of John Nugent Fitch, the first son of Walter's elder brother Alexander and the future lithographer of many plants in *Curtis's Botanical Magazine*.

In March 1841, Sir William was appointed Director of the Royal Botanic Gardens at Kew. He had now become totally dependent on Fitch for illustrating all things botanical, and trusted him absolutely, never questioning his dissections or analyses. Their seven-year association had developed into one of mutual regard and friendship, and it was inevitable therefore that Sir William should wish to take Fitch with him to England. Walter was by now firmly committed to botany, and was delighted to accept Sir William's proposal to leave home and move south.

TWO

1841–1855

The Move to Kew

*F*ITCH ARRIVED AT KEW IN JULY 1841. AT FIRST HE TOOK lodgings nearby, but soon he moved into West Park, the new Hooker home. His studio was on the ground floor, facing north-east, and Sir William, who had no sons at home, relied heavily upon his assistance and company.

Sir William now took up his official duties as Director of the Royal Botanic Gardens, Kew; he was a civil servant, with his salary paid by the government. Walter Fitch, however, was employed directly by Sir William, just as Sir Joseph Banks had employed 'his' artist, Francis Bauer. Bauer held the title of 'Botanick Painter to the King', but when he died in December 1840, this title died with him. Fitch therefore received neither royal glory nor official recognition, but was quite unconcerned, for he had given his allegiance to Sir William and was content with a salary of £100 a year.

Under the directorship of Sir William, the vision of a botanical garden that would also serve as a centre of plant knowledge for the Empire began to materialise. One of Sir William's greatest collectors was to be his own son Joseph, who was still collecting and drawing Antarctic specimens. The plants

West Park

and their descriptions would eventually find their way back to Kew, accompanied by personal letters and rough sketches of Antarctic scenery for Fitch to copy and improve. In February 1842, Prince Albert asked to see Joseph's drawings, which had by then been copied by Fitch. Sir William took them to the Palace, where the Prince showed two of them to the Queen, returning 'with expressions of the Queen's pleasure', and Sir William promptly offered to have copies of them made for Her Majesty.

This entailed yet more work for Fitch, who was already busy with the *Genera Filicum*, the *Journal of Botany*, the *Icones Plantarum*, Hooker's *British Flora*, the *Botanical Magazine* and a new work, *Species Filicum*. He was still drawing Antarctic landscapes and flora for Joseph. He sorely needed a rest, and in August 1842 he went home to Scotland for a holiday, and to attend the baptism of his new niece Elizabeth.

Sir William was meanwhile considering his own position as editor of *Curtis's Botanical Magazine*. When he had taken over the post in 1826, the magazine was a dying concern, but by providing more detailed dissections, and by introducing plants of important economic value such as the fig, clove and nutmeg, he revived it, even though the owner, Samuel Curtis, was planning to sell it.

By the time Fitch returned from Glasgow in the autumn of 1842, the fate of the *Botanical Magazine* was still uncertain, but Walter, who had been the sole artist for nearly eight years, continued to draw plates for its future in a style that had changed from correct botanical drawing to robust yet accurate representation of living plants.

He also resumed his work on the Antarctic flora and scenery, including two seascapes of HMS *Erebus* and HMS *Terror* in the pack ice. These large watercolours, framed in wood taken from the damaged rudder of the *Erebus*, still exist today, in a private collection. These and other watercolours based on Joseph's rough sketches were admired by the many visitors who came to West Park, for Sir William was determined that his son's labours abroad should not go unnoticed.

Joseph returned to England in September 1843, and was soon home at West Park for the first time. The next month, the Queen and Prince Albert came to Kew to meet him and asked to see more of his drawings, either at Buckingham Palace or at Windsor. This time it was Fitch's watercolours of the *Erebus* and *Terror* in the pack ice that caught the royal attention.

In March 1844, the Admiralty agreed to pay Joseph £1000 for the production of 500 plates for *The Botany of the Antarctic Voyage*, with an initial payment after the publication of the first seventy-five. Lovell Reeve, a young, enthusiastic publisher, was eager to take on the work, for as the Admiralty was paying Joseph, he would not have to pay author's fees. Fitch was not paid, either, as the plates were seen as part of his work for Sir William. The

Lovell Reeve

agreement between Reeve and Joseph Hooker, signed in April 1844, marked the beginning of a long relationship between this publishing house, the Hookers and Fitch, and a connection with botany which lasted for over 100 years. It was estimated that the publication would take at least five and a half years to complete, and when the first part was published on 1 June 1844, it received favourable reviews.

By now, Sir William was so disenchanted with the lack of profit from the *Botanical Magazine* that he talked of starting another journal featuring the plants at Kew. Instead, at the end of July, he undertook the first *Popular Guide to the Royal Botanic Gardens at Kew*, and Fitch produced for it sixty-one small and charming woodcuts of many of the plants in the gardens.

The *Botanical Magazine*, in the mean time, struggled on until the end of the year, when Curtis agreed to continue for only another twelve months – an important decision for Fitch, for its closure would have threatened his livelihood and increasing fame.

Early in 1845, Joseph Hooker made a short visit to the Jardin des Plantes in Paris. He was surprised at the difference in the terms of employment offered to botanical artists there, and was not impressed by the work he saw. He wrote to his father: 'had you not better try to secure Fitch to the gardens somehow . . . I think you ought to have something in view for [him] lest he grow too wise.' Joseph was obviously beginning to realise the full value of Fitch's association with his father, and just how necessary Fitch was to the success of his own book, *The Botany of the Antarctic Voyage*.

Once back from France, Joseph set about giving Fitch his due share of glory, and named a new genus of aborescent Compositae after him: 'I have named it [*Fitchia nutans*] in honour of one who is well known as a most accurate and elegant Botanical artist, Mr Walter Fitch'. Fitch was pleased to receive public recognition for his hours of labour on the Hookers' behalf – and even more pleased to receive an additional £25 in salary from Sir William, raising his annual income to £125.

Lovell Reeve, still riding the wave of enthusiasm for *The Botany of the Antarctic Voyage*, made an offer for *Curtis's Botanical Magazine* in February 1845. He was his own printer and publisher, and intended to print the plates by lithography. Terms were agreed in June, and Fitch faced the extra task of lithographing the six plates every month. If a plant was too rare to be transported, he would travel to its place of growth and make minimal sketches *in situ*, return to West Park and rely upon his strong visual memory to complete the drawings, finally drawing them on to the lithographic stone. He was so confident of his ability to draw a plant quickly and accurately, however, that whenever possible he avoided this lengthy process and drew directly on to the stone. The lithographic process is one that leaves little room for error, but Fitch's natural accuracy ensured that he coped with the increased work-load efficiently.

The Botany of the Antarctic Voyage, however, suffered many setbacks in its production, and plates were being spoiled during the printing and colouring. In addition, Joseph could not cope with the discipline of deadlines, causing great problems for Reeve, but by the end of April 1845 the first volume, *Flora Antarctica*, in ten parts, was completed.

Fitch never ceased drawing and painting: in 1845 alone he drew over 200 botanical plates, and yet managed to find the time for work of a more light-hearted nature, including a fine watercolour of cattle grazing in the Old Deer Park at Kew. In the following year, he tackled some large drawings of the royal water-lily, *Victoria amazonica*, a spectacular aquatic plant, with flowers 15 in wide, and leaves over 6 ft across with a 4-in high rim.

That year, seeds of the plant had been brought from Bolivia and sown at Kew. Sir William, anticipating the success of this venture, decided to publish drawings of the plant in the *Botanical Magazine*. Fitch reconstructed preserved specimens of the plant, and produced four lithographs which formed the whole of the January 1847 issue, including one of the few landscapes ever to appear in the magazine. Sadly, the specimens grown from seed at Kew did not survive, but Fitch's brilliant reconstruction aroused great public interest, and the race to raise the *Victoria* at home was now on.

Joseph Hooker was eager to travel again, and November saw him *en route* to India on a botanical expedition, unaware that trouble was brewing at home, for Fitch had returned from a short holiday in Scotland refreshed but rebellious. His friends had pointed out that the Hookers were capitalising on his skill and speed as an artist and lithographer. More importantly, he had expected his salary to continue for the time he was on holiday but Sir William had thought otherwise.

Fitch had now been with Sir William for fifteen years; theirs was an association born of mutual respect and affection, and Fitch's notice of resignation came as a shattering blow to Hooker. He realised that he could not manage without Fitch's services: 'I am too old to break in another young artist, even if I could meet with a suitable lad . . . I have all his work besides for the *Icones*, the *Journal* and *Species Filicum*, to say nothing of the advantage Joseph has received from Fitch's talents . . . if please God, Joseph returns, he will be glad of his services again . . . He is too useful a man to lose.' He offered Fitch a rise in salary to £150 – still not a large amount – but Fitch appreciated the gesture, and agreed to stay.

He was now achieving such fame as a botanical artist that Reeve considered that his name would be bound to increase the sale of any works he illustrated. Consequently Fitch, who had always been known as 'Sir William's artist', now began to illustrate works by other authors. The first of these, *The Popular History of British Sea-Weeds* (1849), was by the Reverend David Landsborough. In September 1848, Fitch, Landsborough and Harvey (a botanist friend of the Hooker family) began the project together at West Park, aided by specimens in Sir William's herbarium. Fitch designed twenty small square plates to be lithographed in sets of four on each of five quarto stones – each stone to print a separate colour: purple, olive, red, green and grey. This was the first time that Fitch had charged for his work independently, and Lovell Reeve paid him £10.

This did not, however, interfere with his other commitments, for he and Sir William were working together on Joseph's behalf. Letters were arriving regularly from Joseph in India, with drawings of new species of rhododendron and magnolia that he had discovered. Sir William had plans for a glorious book on these plants, a large prestigious volume that would impress the world and perpetuate his son's name. Fitch could not resist Sir William's enthusiasm, and they embarked on the project together. Fitch excelled himself on these lithographs, and turned Joseph's basic field sketches into drawings of great botanical beauty.

In December 1848 the first plate was ready, and Sir William wrote: 'Both in execution and subject Rhod. Dalhousiae is the finest I think I ever saw.' Harvey, too, had received a proof: 'What a magnificent thing! I am very impatient to see the book.'

The following February, a new consignment of seeds of *Victoria amazonica* arrived at Kew, and this time three young plants survived. One was given to the Duke of Northumberland at Syon, and another to the Duke of Devonshire at Chatsworth. Joseph Paxton, head gardener at Chatsworth, cossetted his plant by keeping it in a specially heated water tank, and it duly flowered in November 1849, long before the plants at Syon and Kew. The Duke of Devonshire triumphantly sent a flower and leaf to the Queen, pleased to have defeated 'Poor Hooker at Kew.'

Not unnaturally, Hooker was annoyed, especially as it was he who had germinated the seed of this first plant to flower 'in captivity', so when the plant belonging to the Duke of Northumberland also flowered, Sir William wrote to Harvey, 'Victoria . . . has not chosen to flower with anyone below the grade of a Duke'!

The flowers of *Victoria amazonica* caused a sensation, and Walter Fitch, still revelling in the large rhododendron plates, told Sir William that he would like to produce something equally showy for the royal water-lily. Sir William agreed – he may have lost the race for the first flower, but no one, not even a duke, had Fitch to perpetuate its memory. It was arranged for Walter to visit Syon House, where the Duchess of Northumberland allowed him to work in the hothouse that contained their *Victoria*.

The drawings were very large (28 in by 23 in) so that Fitch could portray the flowers full size. They were destined for another grand book, of proportions that matched the splendour of the plant. This time the book was to be Fitch's own, with descriptions by Sir William; it was published by Lovell Reeve, who paid Walter 8 guineas for the four lithographs. Fitch dedicated the book 'To Her Grace the Duchess of Northumberland by whose condescending permission the greater number of original drawings were made in her Grace's stove at Syon. The accompanying plates are with the like permission, most respectfully dedicated by Her Grace's very obedient and faithful servant, Walter Fitch, Kew, February 1st 1851'.

This is Fitch's largest work, but not his best; his original drawings are better than the final lithographs, in which the outlines are perhaps a little too harsh. Nevertheless, it made this sensational plant known throughout the world, and when the *Victoria* finally flowered at Kew, people flocked in their thousands to see it. 'Victoria', said Sir William', 'is all the go'.

Fitch was, of course, still working on Joseph's rhododendrons, and busy copying other non-botanical work – mainly portraits of Joseph in his Indian setting. 'I take it for granted', wrote Joseph, 'that you will get Fitch to copy it'!

At last, in April 1849, the first part of the *Rhododendrons of Sikkim-Himalaya* was published, to enthusiastic reviews. It reached Darjeeling at the beginning of 1850. 'All the Indian world', wrote Joseph proudly, 'is in love with my Rhododendron book . . . it is altogether above notice from the like of me – the plate of *R. Argenteum* likes me the best, and is, I think, not to be surpassed for drawing, perspective, colouring and portraiture'.

Fitch's work had covered a great variety of styles and challenges in the period 1849–51. Forever versatile, he could switch from one type of work to another with the greatest of ease. At the same time as he was portraying the huge flowers of *Victoria amazonica* life size, for instance, he was also fitting whole trees and landscapes into areas of 5 in by 6 in for Mary Roberts's *Voices from the Woodlands* (1850), one of Reeve's Popular Natural History series. Each of these twenty delicately coloured lithographs represents a rural English scene somewhat reminiscent of a minute Gainsborough, although the trees themselves are barely recognisable and so un-Fitchian that one would not suspect that this is the work of a dedicated botanical artist.

Joseph Hooker in the Himalayas
(engraved from a contemporary painting by Frank Stone)

With Joseph's return from India imminent, Fitch moved out of West Park, his home for nearly ten years. He took lodgings at 2 Cumberland Place, in Kew, but still retained his studio at West Park, where he completed the illustrations for *The Popular History of British Ferns* (1851), by Thomas Moore. 'In the work before us', said the *Gardeners' Chronicle*, 'the plates have been drawn on stone by Mr Fitch, who is now without a rival among English botanical draughtsmen.'

The last weeks of 1851 brought financial and professional worries for Sir William – in December Reeve said that he could no longer carry on with the *Icones Plantarum*, which was losing money, and proposed to conclude it in March 1852.

The *Botanical Magazine* was also in financial difficulties, since its circulation continued to decrease, Sir William's written material was slow in reaching the printers, and Reeve found it difficult to publish on time. The solution was either a reduction of Sir William's fees, or a total change in the content and management of the magazine. The most profitable answer, for Reeve at least, would have been to turn it into a more popular work, to suit the requirements of the time, but Sir William preferred to drop his own fees from £18 to £15 a month rather than alter the format and character of the magazine.

Although Joseph returned triumphant from India, he still had his commitment to the Admiralty, and had to resume work on the second part of *The Botany of the Antarctic Voyage – Flora Novae-Zelandiae*. Fitch had only recently put all his enthusiasm into the *Rhododendrons of Sikkim-Himalaya*, for which he had received neither public recognition nor extra payment. He now applied what we would today recognise as a 'work-to-rule' on Joseph's book. Joseph complained to Harvey, 'I would lithograph my own plates if Reeve would not object, but he . . . depends a good deal on Fitch's name for the sale'.

Joseph actually tried his hand at lithography for *The Botany of the Voyage of HMS Herald* (1852–7) for Berthold Seemann but, in spite of his opinion that he could do the plates 'before breakfast', he found lithography far too difficult, and had to admit 'we are all apt to get our little wannities [*sic*] hurt – mine are outraged by Fitch having to draw and lithograph Seemann's plates after all!'

By the summer of 1852, Fitch was still conducting his own one-man go-slow on the *Flora Novae-Zelandiae*, Joseph was peeved by his own failure on Seemann's work, and Sir William was becoming unable to cope with the demands of his herbarium on top of his Kew duties. It was time for a rest from the pressures and problems of publishing. Sir William was content to relax at home, but Joseph and his wife, Harvey, Thomson (a botanist friend of the Hookers) and Fitch went off on holiday to Switzerland.

Fitch enjoyed the break, and the company of Harvey and the Hookers, but he could not afford to work for Joseph without payment, and needed other sources of income. On October 13 1852, two weeks after his return from Switzerland, he agreed with Lovell Reeve on a fee of £20 for selecting and preparing plants and then lithographing twenty plates for *Popular Economic Botany* (1853), by Thomas Archer.

As for Joseph's work, nothing had changed. 'I am regularly stuck in Flora of New Zealand for want of Fitch,' he wailed. Fitch's refusal to work without payment had begun to show, and only ten plates were published in the whole of 1853; however, since seventy plates in all had been completed, Joseph was able to apply for some of his government grant, at £2 a plate. There was only one way to get Fitch back to work, and Joseph finally accepted that 'Sir William's artist' was not unreasonable in expecting payment from Sir William's son! Out of the £2 that Joseph received for each plate from the government, he paid Fitch 30 shillings.

Reeve's Popular Natural History series continued to provide Fitch with a regular source of income, and to bring his name before a much wider public. Archer's *Popular Economic Botany*, a fascinating volume describing the uses of plants for food, clothing, dyeing, etc., was so well received that an abridged edition – *First Steps in Economic Botany* (1854) – was produced for use in schools.

Other botanists and publishers now began to approach Fitch. Many regarded him as the best botanical artist in Europe and, equally important, the quickest. He worked much like a photocopying machine, with the ability to make an exact copy of an original, and to enlarge or reduce it; but unlike a machine, he could also produce original drawings from both living and dried plants, and could dissect and analyse, or even work from descriptions or memory alone.

Now aged thirty-six, he was still earning £150 a year from Sir William, plus about £50 from Joseph and £20 from Reeve. He knew that by charging directly for his work he could earn far more than by working merely as 'Sir William's artist' but although he wanted to be independent, he could not desert Joseph now. *The Botany of the Antarctic Voyage* was their first major work together, and Walter felt it was his duty to see it through to the end – even though it was far more exciting to work on the sketches from Joseph's Indian travels.

Joseph took it for granted that Walter would transform these sketches into paintings suitable for public perusal, and Fitch tackled them with enthusiasm. In the seventy drawings, he returned to his first love – the painting of landscapes – using watercolours and sepia pen-and-wash drawings that display a confident and energetic line. Fitch altered Joseph's original drawings drastically, adding and subtracting features where he felt necessary, and often making a composite drawing out of three or four of Joseph's sketches.

The Queen and Prince Albert took as great an interest in the Indian expedition as they had in the Antarctic one, and again requested Sir William to show them the finished Fitch drawings, the best of which were lithographed and printed in coloured lithotints to illustrate Joseph's *Himalayan Journals* (1854).

For many years the *Icones Plantarum* had provided occupation during the winter months for Sir William and Fitch. They had continued to work on it regardless of the fact that it had temporarily ceased publication in 1854. In June 1854, the *Gardeners' Chronicle* mourned its demise: 'We see with a real regret that this most useful work has terminated . . . No English publication contains so long a series of uniformly good figures of plants'. The tenth volume, with 100 plates by Fitch, was indeed the last – at least for another thirteen years.

The following month, the *Gardeners' Chronicle* announced the forthcoming publication of another new work. Undaunted by the lack of any public acknowledgement for his magnificent illustrations of Joseph Hooker's *Rhododendrons of Sikkim-Himalaya*, or of the scenery in his *Himalayan Journals*, Fitch was now hard at work preparing twenty-five lithographs for a third Indian work.

When *Illustrations of Himalayan Plants* appeared in July 1855, Joseph Hooker at last gave Fitch the credit he was due, and acknowledged his contribution to both the Indian flower books: 'I have been so fortunate as to secure the services of Mr Fitch . . . It has been one of my purest sources of gratification to find that the fruits of my own Himalayan journeys have . . . afforded Mr Fitch the means of executing in the "Illustrations of the Sikkim Rhododendrons" a series of drawings that have been justly pronounced as unrivalled excellence in an artistic point of view. No pains have been spared by the same incomparable Botanical Artist to render the plates now published worthy of imitation'.

For the title page of the book, Fitch created a design of thirty different species of Himalayan flora. Other pages, vibrant with colour, illustrate such plants as the purple *Magnolia campbellii*, or the *Quercus lamellosa*.

The Victorians loved superlatives, and they loved this book. Not only did it contain Fitch's best work, but it was also one of the finest flower books ever produced. It created a sensation in 1855 when it sold for 5 guineas, and in 1990 a copy sold for £10,000!

The *Gardeners' Chronicle* was lavish in its praise: 'Of the merits of the plates it is difficult indeed to speak too highly. Undoubtedly they are the finest that have ever yet been prepared by an English artist; nor are they in any degree inferior to the drawing of the celebrated Austrian Bauers'. Both Her Majesty and Prince Albert subscribed to the work – the crowning accolade for this superb book.

· THREE ·

1856–1892
Frustrations and Achievements

*T*HE YEAR 1856 SAW THE BEGINNING OF A LONG AND
fruitful association between Walter Fitch and the Linnean Society, for
whose publications he produced, often double-quarto size, some of his best
lithographs. In January 1857, Harvey was elected a Fellow of the Society, and
it comes as no surprise to find that in February Fitch was also proposed for
fellowship. Joseph Hooker wrote out the citation himself, and Fitch was
elected a Fellow on 7 April 1857.

This new status gave him the confidence to propose to Hannah Toghill,
from Richmond, but he needed to improve his finances, for the wedding was
to be at the end of the year. He agreed to supply eight coloured plates for each
issue of yet another fern book for Sir William – *Filices Exoticae* (1857–9)
– although he was fully engaged in other work for Sir William, and in
completing Joseph's *Flora Tasmaniae*. Fitch was now so overworked that he
needed an assistant, and he began to instruct his nephew John Nugent Fitch
(now sixteen years old) in botanical drawing and lithography.

In November, Walter completed a work that had been in preparation for
some eighteen months: *A Series of 9 Botanical Drawings* (1857) by J S Henslow,
produced by the government for use in schools. This was something of an
experiment, for the coloured figures were printed on sheets 40 in by 30 in,
making it impractical to use a litho stone, so Fitch drew directly on to a huge
zinc plate. The £10 he received for this helped somewhat towards his wedding
expenses, and he married Hannah on 5 December. Sir William gave Fitch a
writing-box, inlaid with silver; it is made of highly polished, highly grained
wood – could this, like the frames of the seascapes mentioned in chapter 2,
have come from the rudder of HMS *Erebus*?

Mr and Mrs Walter Fitch moved into their first home at 3 Park Cottages,
still in Kew Road, where their first child, also named Walter, was born on 15
September 1858. But the new father was somewhat preoccupied with his
ceaseless drawings of ferns – sixty plates for Sir William's *Species Filicum*
(1846–64), a work similar in size and format to the *Icones Plantarum* and 100
plates for the new quarto work, *Filices Exoticae*. This was a complete departure
from the plainer style of the usual fern books, and contained several fine
examples of Fitch's ability in design. The colouring, too, is more exciting than
the dull green exhibited in most Victorian fern works.

A friend of Walter's, and a fellow member of the Linnean Society was John Eliot Howard (1807–1883), a pharmacologist and botanist, and the largest quinine manufacturer in England. He wanted to produce a book illustrating the original specimens of the *Cinchona* tree, the source of quinine, which had been collected in Peru by a Spanish expedition in 1777. These specimens still survived in the Royal Museum in Madrid, but the only person who could successfully resurrect them, and then produce drawings of them as living plants, was Fitch. Walter was delighted at this further opportunity to travel, and began to make preparations to go, but other commitments interfered with his plans. Harvey was working on the last of the plates for the Antarctic trilogy, and Joseph, not trusting the colouring to anyone but Fitch, somehow persuaded Walter to delay his visit to Spain until Harvey had finished.

Fitch had plenty of work to get on with, and after a delay of four months, he finally received Harvey's patterns, coloured them – and left for Spain the same day, where he was soon at work reviving the dusty 18th-century specimens of Peruvian plants.

Part 1 of Howard's *Illustrations of Nueva Quinologia of Pavon* was published by Reeve on 13 August 1859, and completed by 1862. It was a large folio publication in which Fitch made the most of the shiny leaves, similar in appearance to the laurel. The colouring of the tiny flowers was apparently left to his imagination, causing some controversy in the correspondence columns of the *Gardeners' Chronicle*.

But Fitch had little time to worry about the dispute, for he and Joseph were anxious to finish the *Flora Tasmaniae*, finally published on 29 December 1859. This completed the trilogy of *The Botany of the Antarctic Voyage*. Fitch had completed almost 500 plates over the fifteen and a half years, not five and a half as originally estimated by Sir William. His commitment to Joseph Hooker was over at last.

Early in 1860, Sir William wished to 'secure Fitch to the Gardens'; he therefore proposed that Fitch receive an annual salary of £100 plus an official residence for making an agreed number of finished drawings of the more interesting plants at Kew. This arrangement would suit everyone: Kew would retain Fitch's talents, whilst Fitch would be free of the financial worry of providing a larger house for his family, yet would still be able to work for himself. But the government decided not to employ an official artist in residence at Kew, and the request was denied. Sir William was so confident of eventually getting his own way that Fitch continued to produce the drawings for Kew, for which he received no extra payment.

Sir William's insistence on finished drawings for the Library gave Fitch much extra and unnecessary work. It is true that some of them were used as a basis for the lithographs in the *Botanical Magazine*, but Fitch was now so efficient at drawing plants accurately that he hardly found it necessary to make any preliminary sketches – indeed, as we have seen, he often drew directly on to the stone. Yet after he had completed the lithographs for publication, he was then required to go back and either complete his original sketches, or produce entirely new drawings from scratch. As long as he was paid by Sir William, Fitch felt honour bound to finish the sketches, but he begrudged the time spent on them.

Sir William, now seventy-five and unwell, was inclined to be crotchety. He was in a constant state of disagreement with Reeve – often with good reason – over the *Botanical Magazine*, and was also irritated by the fact that Reeve himself had produced a new work, the *Floral Magazine*. Because this contained illustrations of garden flowers, Reeve did not consider it to be competition for the *Botanical Magazine*, but when the first number appeared on 5 May 1860, edited by Thomas Moore and illustrated by Fitch, Sir William was furious.

Fitch became embroiled in further arguments when Reeve offered to pay him directly for his work on the *Botanical Magazine*. This would also mean that Fitch would not have to waste his valuable time in finishing the drawings for Kew. He badly needed the higher income – his second child Hannah Catherine had been born on 4 February – and so he accepted, and became self-employed. Although he was no longer paid by Sir William on a regular basis, their alliance continued, and he was to carry on illustrating Sir William's fern works for an agreed fee. It is likely that Sir William now played upon old loyalties, and was convincing in his arguments that an official residence and grant would eventually be given to Fitch, for he somehow managed to persuade him to continue finishing the drawings for Kew without any payment.

In the mean time, Fitch had already moved (at his own expense) with his young family and his nephew John to a larger home, Clayton House, on Kew Green.

1860 brought a cold and wet spring and summer, which was to continue into an excessively severe winter. Luckily for Fitch, the wet weather was especially favourable to the growth of fungi, and he drew 150 species for *Outlines of British Fungology* by the Reverend Miles Berkeley. This was published in September, with at least ten small drawings on each of the twenty-four octavo plates.

The following year found Walter working harder than ever to support his ever-growing family, with plates for the new *Floral Magazine*, the *Botanical Magazine*, and Linnean Society publications. In April, another daughter was born, but that same month Fitch suffered his first set-back as a freelance artist. Lovell Reeve was compelled to make major changes to save the *Floral Magazine*, and asked both the artist and editor to resign. The illustrations in the first volume of the *Floral Magazine* display none of the usual Fitch character – perhaps he never really felt at home with the brief he had been given, for he was after all much more a 'botanical' artist than a 'floral' one.

He had no time to bewail his loss of income, however, for Sir William's ferns kept him busy: sixty-six plates for *British Ferns*, followed in 1862 by another sixty-six for *Garden Ferns*.

This same year saw the start of Robert Warner's *Select Orchidaceous Plants*, a work which was to occupy Fitch for sixteen years. These folio plates are some of his finest work, and he revelled in the space they provided to indulge in a more expansive and flamboyant line. The reviews were eulogistic: 'Fitch's admirable drawings are its glory' and 'The Bauers themselves never surpassed Fitch's drawings of the three last [plates]'. To surpass the Bauers was indeed praise of the highest order.

A glance at the list of Fitch's work for 1862 reveals that Hooker publications feature less and less – he embarked, for instance, on the *Florist and Pomologist*, for which he would eventually complete 300 illustrations – but no 'official' announcement had been made stating that Fitch had left Hooker's employ. Many botanists did not know that Fitch was now freelance, and those who did were a little wary of approaching him direct: 'The Hookers were so jealous of my doing any work for others that an idea was prevalent that their approval or permission was necessary.' The majority of Fitch's contacts came from the Linnean Society or from Lovell Reeve; he and Fitch worked well together, for theirs was an association that brought profit to both.

In 1864, Sir William finally finished *Species Filicum*, his great work on ferns, with over 250 plates by Fitch, and immediately embarked on another – *Synopsis Filicum*. Both works remain standard sources of reference.

Fitch had by now completed the monumental number of illustrations required for Bentham's *Handbook of the British Flora* – 1295 in all. These were unpretentious line-drawings of every species included in the Flora, and he represented every plant, irrespective of natural size, within a uniformly small space. The final part of the illustrated edition of the *Handbook of the British Flora* was published in 1865, and it is still in print as a facsimile edition today. As busy as ever, he then produced twenty out of 100 plates for a new quarto work, *Flora Vitiensis* (1865–73), by Berthold Seemann. He was still just as busy increasing his family, and his fifth child, Charles Henry, was born in April.

On 12 August, Sir William Hooker died. In spite of the fact that he was over eighty, his death came unexpectedly to those who were close to him. Sir William had been such a pillar of strength at Kew, such a byword for botany for so long, that it was simply impossible to believe he was gone.

Fitch heard the news with a heavy heart. His friendship with Sir William had lasted thirty-three years, and in the whole of that time there had been scarcely a single day when they did not have some form of contact. Fitch's

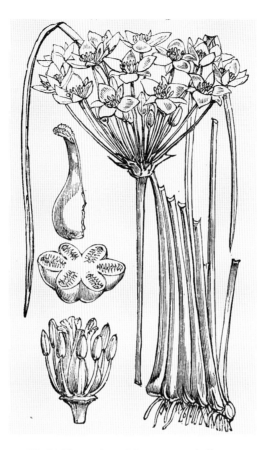

Fitch's Illustration of *Butomus umbellatus,*
for George Bentham's *Handbook of the British Flora*

allegiance to Sir William had been profound and undivided – he had shared
his home, and taken his advice and admonitions like a son.

Sir William was buried in the churchyard of St Anne's Kew, and in the
church a handsome Wedgwood tablet commemorates him. Around his profile
are arrangements of wheat and grasses designed by Fitch: Walter's last act of
devotion and his last work on ferns for Sir William Jackson Hooker. An
obituary in the *Gardeners' Chronicle* contained the following lines: 'In
connection with the scientific labours of Sir William Hooker, there are two
names which should be prominently mentioned. The one is that of Lady
Hooker, who for 40 years was his able amanuensis and assistant in literary
duties and library; the other is that of Walter Fitch Esq., now the most
distinguished botanical artist in Europe'.

In November, there were two more deaths: John Lindley, who had been
editor of the *Gardeners' Chronicle* since its foundation, and Lovell Reeve, who
had provided Fitch with a continuous supply of work. For Walter, these
deaths severed the last strings of dependence. He respected Joseph as a friend
of some thirty years' standing, but did not feel he owed him the same
allegiance that he had given to Sir William. Joseph had succeeded his father as

Director of Kew Gardens, but was to become more distant, and more autocratic and overbearing, and Sir William's promise to 'secure Fitch to the Gardens' was conveniently forgotten.

Hooker had also succeeded his father as editor of the *Botanical Magazine*, and Francis Soper, a relative and partner of Lovell Reeve, had taken over the firm of Reeve & Co. Soper arranged to pay Fitch £112 for sketching, drawing and lithographing the seventy-two plates in each year's *Botanical Magazine* – less than Walter's usual charge of £2 each.

He had more or less come to terms with the fact that there would be no official residence, although from time to time he prodded Joseph about 'the house'. However, he had been providing the finished drawings for Kew only on the strength of Sir William's promise, and he now told Joseph that he would no longer provide these without payment. Joseph insisted that Fitch finish the drawings and give them to Kew, hinting that, as editor, he had legal rights in the matter. As the *Botanical Magazine* was not an official Kew publication, and as Fitch was paid by the publisher, it is unlikely that Joseph Hooker, who was also paid by the publisher, had any such rights at all.

So why did Fitch not refuse? Possibly he feared losing his income from the magazine, and possibly he was also concerned that his case for an official residence and grant might be closed forever. Fitch felt bound to carry on, but this time it was with very bad grace – he resented the time spent on finishing seventy-two drawings gratis every year for the Kew Library. As a consequence, Fitch lost his enthusiasm for the magazine, and the standard of the plates began to decline. The drawings adequately fulfilled any botanical requirements, but they lacked artistic merit. Where was Fitch's usual panache, his joy in composition, his enthusiasm for leaves and movement? Fitch's lack-lustre execution was not the only criticism to be levelled at the plates; the printing and colouring were judged pale and anaemic. Soper's handling of Lovell Reeve & Co's oldest botanical publication was not encouraging.

After Lindley's death, Maxwell Masters (1833–1907) was appointed editor of the *Gardeners' Chronicle*, which was to become an outlet not only for Fitch's botanical work, but also for his humorous correspondence and personal views on botany and horticulture. The pleasure these activities brought him was soon dampened by the news that his friend William Harvey had died on 5 May; Hooker, Reeve and Harvey – all suddenly gone. Joseph and Walter remained, but some of the strongest emotional links that had held them together, often in an uneasy truce, no longer existed.

In the Fitch household, however, this was not a time for dwelling on the past. John Nugent Fitch, now aged twenty-six, joined forces with his younger brother, Robert Urie Fitch, a lithographic printer. The Fitch brothers operated from Fitzroy Square, and their first known joint work was for the

Linnean Society. From 1866 onwards, most of Walter's work for the Society was printed by John, an artist himself and a skilled and sensitive fine-art lithographer and printer. Walter had total confidence in his nephew's abilities, and the many lithographs which can be seen in the *Transactions of the Linnean Society* are a tribute to this artistic partnership.

Although Fitch was most interested in writing for the *Gardeners' Chronicle*, his first article, on *Camoensia maxima*, was published in *Nature & Art* early in 1867, and was accompanied by his own illustrations. Joseph Hooker, observing perhaps uneasily Fitch's new public persona, decided upon a new venture – to revive the *Icones Plantarum*, the one publication they both loved, which had ceased publication over thirteen years previously.

Fitch was delighted; like Joseph; he had always missed the *Icones Plantarum*, and was never happier than when drawing dried specimens. He considered them a greater challenge than living plants, the drawing of which, he felt, was by comparison mere copying. Fitch alone had been responsible for the illustration of the *Icones Plantarum* from 1836 to 1854, and was now pleased to be able to continue it.

By the autumn of the following year, Fitch had completed sixty-three plates for another new work, *Refugium Botanicum* (1868–73), by W W Saunders. The somewhat sparse drawings, fine examples of Fitch's compositional abilities, were all printed with care by John Fitch and show a confident yet sensitive line. Walter enjoyed this work, of which he was later to say: 'I did almost all the drawings, chiefly from living specimens in Saunder's own collection, from Kew Gardens, and from sundry charitable nurserymen and growers . . . [for] the Refugium was established as an asylum for waifs and strays which would otherwise have died unknown'.

Dr Masters was impressed by Fitch's writing talents, and he commissioned eight articles on the technique of flower drawing for the *Gardeners' Chronicle*; these appeared between January and May 1869, illustrated by small woodcuts of explanatory diagrams and peppered with Fitch's witticisms. They were so well received that they were later translated into French for Continental publications. Fitch was happy to pass on his years of experience, and was emphatic on the difference between botanical drawing and mere flower painting: 'A strictly botanical drawing generally represents but one or two individual plants, and they must be equally correctly drawn and coloured. A fancy drawing or group . . . may have the details judiciously slurred over', and he advised 'that a knowledge of botany, however slight, is of great use in enabling the artist to avoid the errors which are occasionally perpetuated in respectable drawings and publications'.

He wrote, too, on the drawing of leaves and stalks, dissections, analyses and herbarium work – drawings made from dried specimens: 'Sketching living plants is merely a species of copying, but dried specimens test the artist's ability to the uttermost; and by drawings made from them would I be judged as a correct draughtsman'.

Walter had almost given up hope of becoming Kew's official artist, with a government salary and a residence. He now had seven children, and his need to support his family caused him to reflect upon his finances. With his new income from writing, the regular work for *Refugium Botanicum*, plus all his other work, perhaps he could give up the *Botanical Magazine*, for he found Joseph's continuing demands for the finished drawings extremely irksome.

In December 1869, Joseph Hooker, perhaps in an attempt at reconciliation, dedicated the 95th volume of the *Botanical Magazine* 'To Walter Fitch Esq, FLS, The Accomplished Artist and Lithographer of upwards 2,500 plates already published of the Botanical Magazine this volume is dedicated by his faithful and sincere friend Jos. D Hooker'. Fitch was heartened by the dedication and the recognition it gave him, and he stayed on with Joseph and the magazine.

It was just as well that he had decided to stay, for although he had drawn 500 plates for the *Refugium Botanicum*, this ran into financial difficulties and ceased publication, with over 100 of his drawings unused. The *Icones Plantarum*, too, had been temporarily dropped again by the end of 1873, and it seemed after all that the *Botanical Magazine* was to be his only regular source of income, yet he longed to give it up.

The following year the Fitch family moved to 4 Cambridge Terrace, Kew Green, opposite the church. As a light relief from his botanical commitments Fitch began to concern himself with less exacting work for publication. The first example of these 'fancy sketches' appeared in the *Gardeners' Chronicle* in May 1875: 'A study of buds' was a half-page illustration, set in a circular border. It was engraved by Worthington George Smith, an artist friend of Fitch who had worked on the *Gardeners' Chronicle* since 1869. The buds were followed in the same month by 'A primrose by a river's brim', which was produced at the instigation of a member of the paper's staff who had visited Fitch's studio and seen a watercolour 'so charming in its truthfulness' that he begged the artist to reproduce it.

These 'fancy sketches' doubtless provided a much-needed relaxation for Fitch. By 1876 he was in a permanent state of disagreement with Joseph Hooker, who was again insisting that Fitch work up his preliminary sketches into finished drawings for Kew. It is difficult to understand the reasons behind Hooker's insistence, for the drawings were of no particular value (the lithographs did in fact meet every scientific requirement) other than to continue the collection of original watercolours at Kew.

Fitch's eyesight was now deteriorating – yet another reason why he wished to give up work for the *Botanical Magazine*. The plates were relatively small, and mistakes in lithography were difficult to erase. But Walter still enjoyed

'A primrose by a river's brim'
(*Gardeners' Chronicle*, new series, vol III)

large works, and was perfectly able to meet the challenge of producing a prestigious botanical book such as *The Quinology of the East Indian Plantations* (1869–76). This was another work on *Cinchona* plants by John Howard, but this time John Nugent Fitch handled the printing and much of the lithography, producing superb plates that are some of the happiest results of the Fitch partnership.

In January 1877, an agreement was drawn up between Joseph Hooker as editor and Lovell Reeve & Co as proprietors of *Curtis's Botanical Magazine*, the last line of which ran: 'the original sketches or drawings of the plant to remain the property of the said Dr Hooker.' It is doubtful whether Fitch even knew about this new arrangement.

Joseph Hooker received a knighthood in June, and left soon after for a botanising holiday in the Rocky Mountains of Colorado. Fitch spent the summer working on *A Monograph of the Genus Lilium* (a prestige folio work for John Henry Elwes), sundry illustrations for the *Gardeners' Chronicle*, and the daily work for the Linnean Society. As usual, he was producing all the plates for the *Botanical Magazine*, even though he was not being paid regularly. Hooker's insistence on the finished drawings without payment continued to foster resentment in Fitch, and as he approached old age, his bitterness increased. Simply, he was tired of making two drawings for every *Botanical Magazine* plate.

When, in November, Joseph returned exhausted from America, he received this letter from Fitch: 'Dear Sir Joseph. I forward you the three sketches of the 3 Botanical Magazine plates which finish this year, and it is probable that they will be the last. Yours respectfully, Walter Hood Fitch.'

As editor, Sir Joseph must have experienced something bordering on despair, but Fitch relented a little and, out of 'respect for work I have carried on for some 45 years' furnished Soper with material for the February and March numbers, but Fitch had still not been paid by May. It was the final straw: 'My interest is gone in the work in consequence of such treatment'. He would do no more.

Soper had to turn to John Nugent Fitch for help, and February 1878 saw the first plate of the *Botanical Magazine* (pl 6342) lithographed by the younger Fitch, who was to continue until 1920. Other help was needed for the drawing, and Sir Joseph's daughter Harriet, who had been taught by Walter Fitch, produced some admirable drawings, professionally polished by the lithography of John Fitch. In June, drawings appeared by Ann Barnard (Harriet's aunt), various members of the Herbarium staff, and Worthington Smith. By the end of the year, the initials 'MS' began to appear; this was Matilda Smith, a distant cousin of Sir Joseph. Until her abilities as an artist – and her confidence – increased, John Fitch's lithography transformed her amateur drawings into lively portraits of plants, in a style not dissimilar to that of his uncle. To those outside Kew, the great crisis was hardly visible.

Walter Fitch had worked on the *Botanical Magazine* for forty-four years, and had completed 2894 plates. When he resigned, he parted with the financial mainstay of his youth and middle age, yet experienced a curious sense of release.

There was still plenty of work to do: he was working on a third series of Warner's *Select Orchidaceous Plants* (1877–81), gorgeous folios that had been so well received that the public were clamouring for more. Walter completed the first thirteen plates, and another twenty-three were drawn and lithographed by his nephew. He had also completed practically all the plates for the *Lilium* monograph. Drawn with sweeping strokes directly on to the stone, these plates undoubtedly show Fitch's freest work with the lithographic chalk.

A small but regular source of income was still provided by the *Florist and Pomologist*, and another twelve plates a year were commissioned by Fitch's old friend William Botting Hemsley for *Biologia Centrali-Americana* (1879–88). At a meeting of the Royal Horticultural Society in June 1878, Walter showed some coloured drawings of auriculas and roses, and in February 1879 exhibited yet more paintings at the Linnean Society, this time of orchids.

In spite of all this, his volume of work had decreased, and for a time he was tempted to consider a proposal he had received from a publisher to revive a work (the *Botanical Register*) that had been dormant for some years, and which could compete directly with the *Botanical Magazine*. It would have been edited from the British Museum (Natural History), but would have antagonised Sir Joseph and so Fitch dropped the idea. He was, in fact, enjoying himself providing more 'fancy sketches' for the *Gardeners' Chronicle* and working on some articles due for publication that summer. The first, on *Cypripedium calceolus*, appeared in June, followed by 'Foxgloves in the Wild Garden', and 'Wild Roses'. He was rather pleased with these, and wrote a note to Worthington Smith, who was making the wood-engraving for the latest illustration: 'Hope to see the roses soon. I wrote rather a racy scrap about them and hope it will be put in or I shall cock my ink bottle!' The editor obviously approved, but reading it today is not unlike trying to walk through a wordy

'Wild Roses' (*Gardeners' Chronicle*, new series, vol xii)

bramble patch full of literary thorns. There also seems to be a certain amount of cynicism creeping into Fitch's humour.

Free from the restraints of days devoted entirely to botany, Fitch was at last able to indulge in landscape painting. He confided to his nephew that at times he had regretted not following this line, 'but that he had tried to do his duty in the position that it had pleased God to place him.' He was now to be seen strolling around the vicinity of Kew, sketchbook in hand. He captured local scenes, including *The Old Blacksmith's Shop, The 'Eyot' at Kew* and *The City Barge*. In these highly professional paintings, Fitch's compositional skills remain unchallenged and his enjoyment of colour and light is evident.

'The "Eyot" at Kew'
(*Gardeners' Chronicle,* new series, vol XVIII)

Although he had exhibited and sold some of his paintings, he found, like so many artists before him, that he could not live by these alone. He gave lessons in botanical drawing to young ladies, including Matilda Smith, Sir Joseph's new artist, and in desperation even considered selling his life's work, his own extremely rare quarto set of the *Botanical Magazine*. 'Twenty-five volumes, re-touched by myself . . . It is now an encumbrance on my shelves, and would be valuable to any library,' he noted.

On hearing of this, Sir Joseph, who in his own words was a 'faithful and sincere friend', softened and decided to help Walter. Hooker's early career had benefited enormously from Fitch's assistance, and now was the time of reckoning. He prepared a report for Disraeli, the Prime Minister, reminding him that copies of the finest of Fitch's works were housed in the royal libraries of Osborne and Windsor. Hooker also showed him, among other things, the drawings of the royal water-lily, and Disraeli, himself a great royalist, agreed to grant Fitch a government pension.

On 16 April 1880, Fitch received a letter from 10 Downing Street informing him that 'The Queen has been graciously pleased to confer on you a pension of one hundred pounds a year, from Her Majesty's Civil List, in consideration of your services to Botanical Science.'

Fitch immediately wrote to Sir Joseph: 'I feel that I can never thank you too much for your successful efforts on my behalf, and the trouble you have taken, and I trust our misunderstanding (which I much regret) has left no doubt on your mind of my respect for yourself as I had for your father.'

The *Gardeners' Chronicle* was well pleased: 'It is with great satisfaction that we are enabled to announce that a pension . . . from the Civil List has been awarded to Mr W H Fitch . . . There can be but one feeling, that in this matter a very right thing has been done.'

His botanical commitments at Kew were over, but he continued his plant drawings for other botanists – for Hemsley's *Biologia Centrali-Americana*, and for Hiern and Ficalho's *On Central African Plants*. He still contributed plates to the *Gardeners' Chronicle* as well, his *Group of Orchids* on 27 August 1881 exciting enthusiastic reviews from the national press. In 1883 he moved house again, this time to 6 Priory Park Terrace, on the opposite side of Kew Green. By 1885, his contributions to the *Gardeners' Chronicle* had dwindled, although he was still continuously supplied with small amounts of work by his botanical friends. He trained his son Charles in botanical work, and in 1887 the family provided several plates for the *Transactions of the Linnean Society*. These were for Oliver's *The Plants of Kilima-Njaro*, and were drawn by Walter, lithographed by Charles, and printed by John. A veritable hat trick of Fitches!

Suddenly, in 1888, Walter Fitch – now aged seventy-one – decided to move house yet again. The family packed up their belongings, including a pile of portfolios 3 ft high containing much of Walter's non-botanical work, and moved into Llewellyn House, an older, more imposing building next door to King's Cottage, and nearer the more prestigious royal residences. It was opposite St Anne's Church, and more convenient for Fitch, as it backed on to the Melon Yard of the Gardens.

The change of residence gave Fitch a new lease of life. He drew sixteen plates for Balfour's *Botany of Socotra* (1888) and added some more wood-engravings to the fifty-five he had drawn in 1866 for Fairbairn's *Imperial Bible Dictionary*. He even found the energy to take his great-nieces, Elsie and Dora, on a trip up the River Thames to see the Summer Exhibition at the Royal Academy.

He finally finished Hemsley's *Biologia Centrali-Americana*, and in 1890 tackled fifteen wood-engravings for Jackson's *Commercial Botany of the 19th Century*. He then drew and lithographed nine plates for Hart's *Some Account of Flora and Fauna of Sinai*, published the following year. This was to be his last work. He fell ill, and suffered a stroke. On 14 January 1892, aged seventy-four, Walter Hood Fitch, FLS, Botanical Artist and Lithographer extraordinary, died.

In St Anne's church on Kew Green the bell tolled all day in mourning. The church flag was flown at half mast that day – to mark the death of the Duke of Clarence – a coincidental but fitting tribute to Fitch's years of devotion to the Royal Botanic Gardens at Kew.

Walter Fitch and his wife in old age

Works Illustrated by Walter Hood Fitch

This is a list of the major works illustrated by Walter Hood Fitch, arranged in chronological order. Where he was not the sole artist, the dates of his contributions are shown in italics. A much more complete listing of Fitch's work is given in *Kew Bulletin* 1915, pp 277–84.

Curtis's Botanical Magazine	*1834–78*
Companion to the Botanical Magazine	1835–6
William Jackson Hooker	*Botanical Illustrations* (1837)
William Jackson Hooker et al	*Icones Plantarum* (1836–54, 1867–76)
William Jackson Hooker and G A Walker Arnott	*The Botany of Captain Beechey's Voyage* (1830–41) *1837–41*
William Jackson Hooker	*Flora Boreali-Americana* (1829–40) *Vol 2 1837–40*
William Jackson Hooker	*Genera Filicum* (1838–42)
Journal of Botany	(1840–2); continued as *London Journal of Botany* (1842–8); continued as *Hooker's Journal of Botany and Kew Gardens Miscellany* (1849–57)
Joseph Dalton Hooker	*The Botany of the Antarctic Voyage* I *Flora Antarctica* (1844–7) II *Flora Novae-Zelandiae* (1852–5) III *Flora Tasmaniae* (1855–9)
William Jackson Hooker	*Species Filicum* (1846–64)
William Jackson Hooker et al.	*Popular Guide to the Royal Botanic Gardens at Kew* (1844–85) Many issues illustrated by Fitch
David Landsborough	*The Popular History of British Sea-weeds* (1849)
Joseph Dalton Hooker	*Rhododendrons of Sikkim-Himalaya* (1849–51)
Mary Roberts	*Voices from the Woodlands* (1850)
Thomas Moore	*The Popular History of British Ferns* (1851)
Berthold Seemann	*The Botany of the Voyage of H.M.S. Herald* (1852–7)
Thomas Archer	*Popular Economic Botany* (1853); abridged version, *First Steps in Economic Botany* (1854)
Joseph Dalton Hooker	*Himalayan Journals* (1854)
Joseph Dalton Hooker	*Illustrations of Himalayan Plants* (1855)
Transactions of the Linnean Society	1856–87
John Steven Henslow	*A Series of 9 Botanical Drawings* (1857)
William Jackson Hooker	*Filices Exoticae* (1857–9)
John Eliot Howard	*Illustrations of Nueva Quinologia of Pavon* (1859–62)
Floral Magazine	(1861–81) *1860–1*

Miles Joseph Berkeley	*Outlines of British Fungology* (1860)
William Jackson Hooker	*British Ferns* (1861)
William Jackson Hooker	*Garden Ferns* (1862)
Robert Warner	*Select Orchidaceous Plants* (1862–5); 2nd series (1865–75); 3rd series *(1877–81)*
Florist and Pomologist	(1862–84)
William Jackson Hooker and John Gilbert Baker	*Synopsis Filicum* (1868)
George Bentham	*Handbook of the British Flora*, 2nd edn (1865)
Berthold Seemann	*Flora Vitiensis* (1865–73)
Patrick Fairbairn	*Imperial Bible Dictionary* (1866)
William Wilson Saunders	*Refugium Botanicum* (1868–73)
Gardeners' Chronicle	*1855–93*
John Eliot Howard	*The Quinology of the East Indian Plantations* (1869–76)
John Henry Elwes	*A Monograph of the Genus Lilium* (1877–80)
William Botting Hemsley	*Biologia Centrali-Americana* (1879–88)
William Philip Hiern and Count Ficalho	*On Central African Plants* (1881)
Isaac Bailey Balfour	*Botany of Socotra* (1888)
John Reader Jackson	*Commercial Botany of the Nineteenth Century* (1890)
Henry Chichester Hart	*Some Account of Flora and Fauna of Sinai* (1891)

Plates

Plates marked * are reproductions of Fitch's original watercolour drawings; all others are reproductions of published plates. For fuller details of the books listed here, see booklist.

1   *Cattleya dowiana (Curtis's Botanical Magazine,* vol XCIII)*

2   *Hodgsonia macrocarpa* (Joseph Dalton Hooker *Illustrations of Himalayan Plants)*

3   A group of lilies, including *Lilium martagon* var. *cattaniae, L. wallichianum* var. *neilgherrense, L. japonicum, L. brownii, L. humboldtii (Gardeners' Chronicle,* new series, vol IX)

4   *Magnolia candollii* var. *obovata (Illustrations of Himalayan Plants)*

5   *Lilium humboldtii* (John Henry Elwes *A Monograph of the Genus Lilium)*

6   *Meconopsis paniculata (Illustrations of Himalayan Plants)*

7   Cherry 'St Margaret's' *(Florist and Pomologist,* 1881)

8   *Agapetes saligna* and *A. serpens (Illustrations of Himalayan Plants)*

9   *Esmeralda cathcartii (Illustrations of Himalayan Plants)*

10   *Leptocodon gracilis, Codonopsis javanica* and *C. inflata (Illustrations of Himalayan Plants)*

11   *Rhododendron grande* (Joseph Dalton Hooker *Rhododendrons of Sikkim-Himalaya)*

12   *Quercus lamellosa (Illustrations of Himalayan Plants)*

13   *Phalaenopsis schilleriana* var. *splendens* (Robert Warner *Select Orchidaceous Plants)*

14   *Berberis ilicifolia* (Joseph Dalton Hooker *The Botany of the Antarctic Voyage: I, Flora Antarctica)*

15   *Aspidium mohrioides (Botany of the Antarctic Voyage: I, Flora Antarctica)*

16   *Cinchona pitayensis* (John Eliot Howard *The Quinology of the East Indian Plantations)*

17   *Phalaenopsis schilleriana (Select Orchidaceous Plants)*

18   *Paphiopedilum hirsutissimum (Select Orchidaceous Plants)*

19   *Oncidium sarcodes (Select Orchidaceous Plants)*

20   *Barkeria skinneri (Select Orchidaceous Plants)*

21   *Lilium speciosum (Monograph of the Genus Lilium)*

22   *Mimulus lewisii (Curtis's Botanical Magazine,* vol LXI)

23   *Echinocereus polyacanthus* var. *polyacanthus (Curtis's Botanical Magazine,* vol LXXV)*

24   *Rossioglossum grande (Curtis's Botanical Magazine,* vol LXVIII)

25   *Crocus sieberi (Curtis's Botanical Magazine,* vol XCIX)*

26   *Cyclamen persicum* varieties *(Floral Magazine,* vol I)

27   *Paeonia emodi (Curtis's Botanical Magazine,* vol XCIV)*

28   *Rhododendron* sp. *(Rhododendrons of Sikkim-Himalaya)*

29   *Rhododendron hodgsonii (Rhododendrons of Sikkim-Himalaya)*

30   *Rhododendron fulgens (Rhododendrons of Sikkim-Himalaya)*

31   *Lilium bulbiferum (Monograph of the Genus Lilium)*

32   *Cyperus gunnii* and *Schoenus tenuissimus (Botany of the Antarctic Voyage: III, Flora Tasmaniae)*

33   *Lilium monadelphum (Monograph of the Genus Lilium)*

34 *Lilium hansonii (Monograph of the Genus Lilium)*

35 *Iris aphylla (Curtis's Botanical Magazine*, vol xcv)*

36 *Lilium brownii (Monograph of the Genus Lilium)*

37 *Clianthus formosus (Curtis's Botanical Magazine*, vol lxxxiv)*

38 *Lilium leichtlinii* var. *maximowiczii (Monograph of the Genus Lilium)*

39 *Hypericum hookerianum (Curtis's Botanical Magazine*, vol lxxxii)*

40 *Lilium chalcedonicum (Monograph of the Genus Lilium)*

41 *Calycanthus occidentalis (Curtis's Botanical Magazine*, vol lxxx)*

42 *Lilium pomponium (Monograph of the Genus Lilium)* Note: the colour here is as in the published plate. *L. pomponium* is bright red.

43 *Rosa* × *odorata* 'Fortune's Double Yellow' (*Curtis's Botanical Magazine*, vol xxviii)*

44 *Billardiera drummondianus (Curtis's Botanical Magazine*, vol xci)*

45 *Argyreia hirsuta (Curtis's Botanical Magazine*, vol lxxxii)*

46 *Banksia victoriae (Curtis's Botanical Magazine*, vol lxxxii)*

47 *Aquilegia caerulea (Curtis's Botanical Magazine*, vol xc)*

48 *Nymphaea elegans (Curtis's Botanical Magazine*, vol lxxvii)*

49 *Bergenia* × *schmidtii (Curtis's Botanical Magazine*, vol xciii)*

50 *Primula pedemontana (Curtis's Botanical Magazine*, vol xcv)*

51 *Eritrichium nanum (Curtis's Botanical Magazine*, vol xcvi)*

52 *Hibbertia baudouinii (Curtis's Botanical Magazine*, vol xcix)*

53 *Senecio pulcher (Curtis's Botanical Magazine*, vol xciii)*

54 *Acalypha wilkesiana* (Berthold Seemann *Flora Vitiensis*)

55 *Asplenium australasicum* (William Jackson Hooker *Filices Exoticae*)

56 *Meconopsis simplicifolia (Illustrations of Himalayan Plants)*

57 *Rhododendron* × *candelabrum (Rhododendrons of Sikkim-Himalaya)*

58 *Nepenthes veitchii (Curtis's Botanical Magazine*, vol lxxxiv)*

59 × *Seleliocereus fulgidus (Curtis's Botanical Magazine*, vol xcvi)*

60 *Nicotiana fragrans (Curtis's Botanical Magazine*, vol lxxxi)*

61 *Hylocereus lemairei (Curtis's Botanical Magazine*, vol lxxx)*

62 *Cattleya granulosa (Curtis's Botanical Magazine*, vol lxxxiv)*

63 *Nymphaea devoniensis (Curtis's Botanical Magazine*, vol lxxviii)*

64 *Persea americana (Curtis's Botanical Magazine*, vol lxxvii)

65 Apple 'Yellow Bellefleur' (*Florist and Pomologist*, 1884)

66 Fungi, including *Armillaria mellea, Tricholoma equestre, T. imbricatum, T. sulphureum, Calocybe gambosa, T. album, Lepista nuda* (Miles Joseph Berkeley *Outlines of British Fungology*)

67 *Begonia tenera* var. *thwaitesii (Curtis's Botanical Magazine*, vol lxxviii)*

68 *Victoria amazonica* dissections (*Victoria regia; or illustration of the royal water lily, … chiefly from specimens flowering at Syon and at Kew … with description by Sir W J Hooker*, 1851)

69 *Victoria amazonica (Victoria regia …)*

70 *Victoria amazonica*, opening flowers (*Victoria regia …*)

71 *Victoria amazonica*, expanded flower (*Victoria regia …*)

72 Mango Mountain ('Indian Sketches', 1847–54 (unpublished))*

73 *Rhododendron dalhousiae:* sketches by Joseph Dalton Hooker and Walter Hood Fitch and published plate from *Rhododendrons of Sikkim-Himalaya*

Cattleya dowiana

1

Cattleya dowiana

2

Hodgsonia macrocarpa

3

A group of lilies: (bottom left) *Lilium martagon* var. *cattaniae;* (centre) *L. wallichianum* var. *neilgherrense;* (top left) *L. japonicum;* (top right) *L. brownii;* (bottom right) *L. humboldtii*

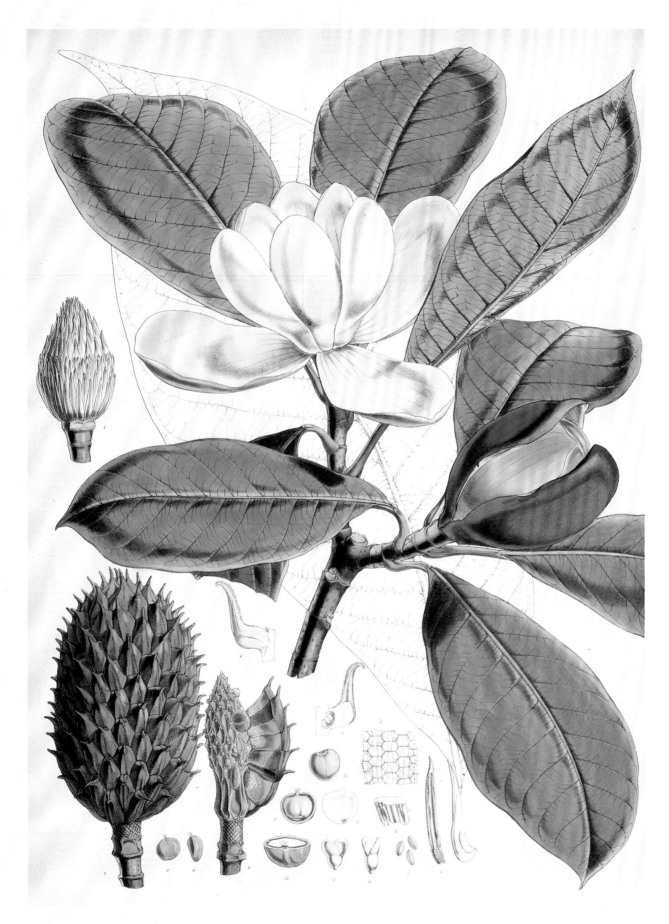

4

Magnolia candollii var. *obovata*

5

Lilium humboldtii

6

Meconopsis paniculata

7

Cherry 'St Margaret's'

8

A *Agapetes saligna*;   B *A. serpens*

Plate XXIII

9

Esmeralda cathcartii

Plate XVI

10

A *Leptocodon gracilis;*   B *Codonopsis javanica;*   C *C. inflata*

Tab. IX

J.H.D. del. Fitch lith.

Reeve, Benham & Reeve, imp.

11

Rhododendron grande

12

Quercus lamellosa

W H Fitch, del et lith

Vincent Brook, Day & Son Imp

13

Phalaenopsis schilleriana var. *splendens*

14

Berberis ilicifolia

15

Aspidium mohrioides

16

Cinchona pitayensis

Plate I

17

Phalaenopsis schilleriana

Plate XV

W.H.Fitch, del. et lith.

Vincent Broos. sc. imp.

Cypripedium hirsutissimum

18

Paphiopedilum hirsutissimum

Plate XXIII

W.H.Fitch,del et lith.

Viricent Brooks,Imp.

Oncidium sarcodes

19

Oncidium sarcodes

Plate XXXVIII.

20

Barkeria skinneri

21

Lilium speciosum

22

Mimulus lewisii

23

Echinocereus polyacanthus var. *polyacanthus*

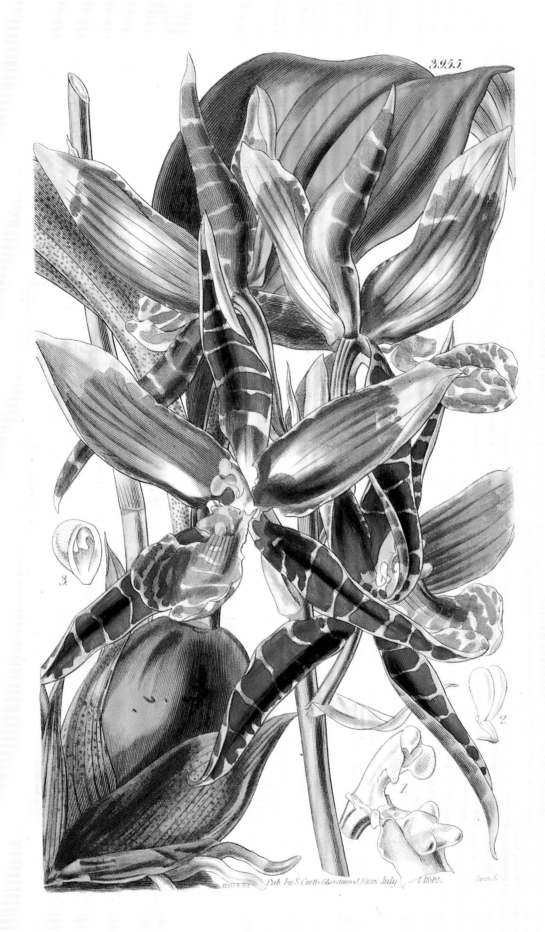

Pub. by S. Curtis Glazenwood Essex July 1 1842.

24

Rossioglossum grande

25

Crocus sieberi

26

Cyclamen persicum varieties

27

Paeonia emodi

J.D.H. del. Fitch lith.

Reeve, Benham & Reeve, imp.

28

Rhododendron sp.

29

Rhododendron hodgsonii

30

Rhododendron fulgens

31

Lilium bulbiferum

32

Cyperus gunnii (left) and *Schoenus tenuissimus* (right)

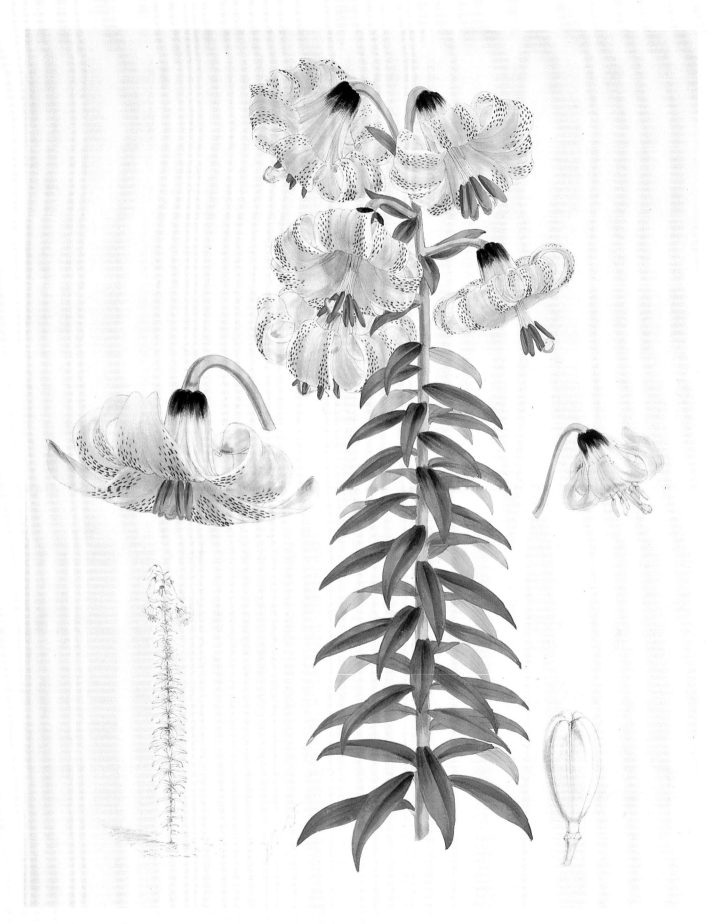

33

Lilium monadelphum

34

Lilium hansonii

35

Iris aphylla

36

Lilium brownii

37

Clianthus formosus

38

Lilium leichtlinii var. *maximowiczii*

39

Hypericum hookerianum

40

Lilium chalcedonicum

Bot. Mag.

41

Calycanthus occidentalis

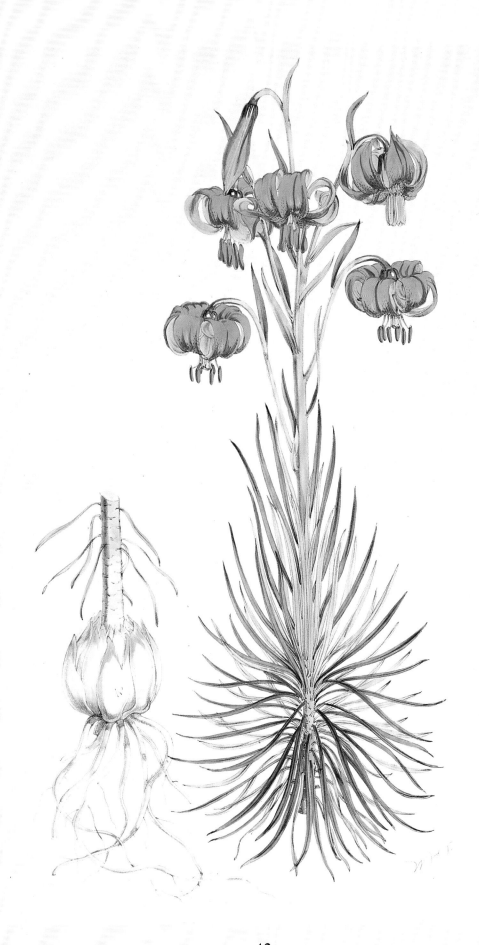

42

Lilium pomponium

43

Rosa × odorata 'Fortune's Double Yellow'

44

Billardiera drummondianus

45

Argyreia hirsuta

46

Banksia victoriae

47

Aquilegia caerulea

48

Nymphaea elegans

49

Bergenia × schmidtii

50

Primula pedemontana

51

Eritrichium nanum

52

Hibbertia baudouinii

53

Senecio pulcher

54

Acalypha wilkesiana

Plate LXXXVIII

55

Asplenium australasicum

Plate VI

56

Meconopsis simplicifolia

57

Rhododendron × candelabrum

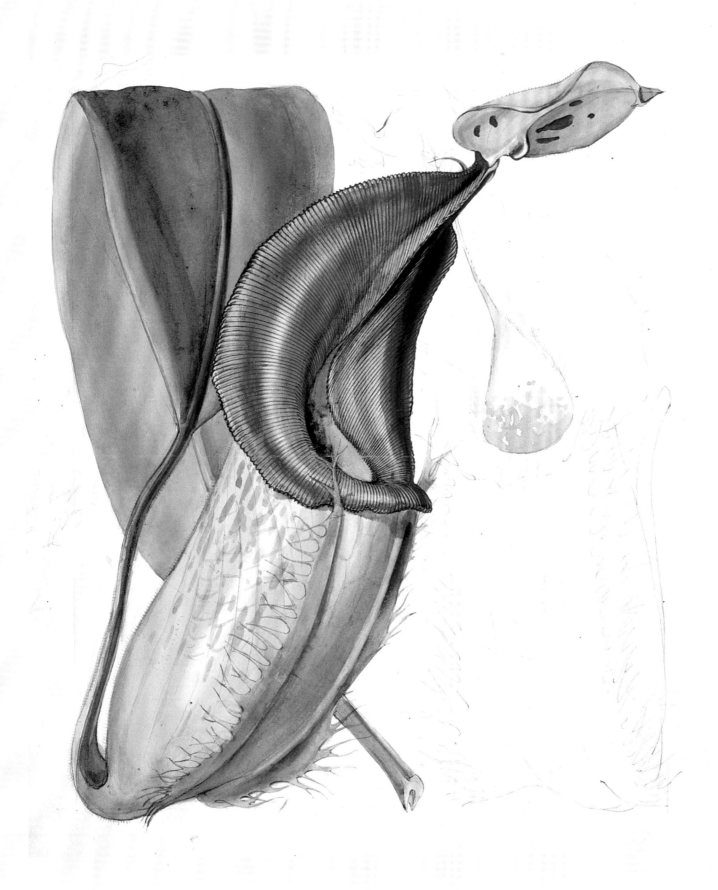

58

Nepenthes veitchii

Cereus fulaidus Hook

59

× *Seleliocereus fulgidus*

Leaf not to be coloured.   Nicotiana fragrans, Hook.

60

Nicotiana fragrans

61

Hylocereus lemairei

62

Cattleya granulosa

4665.

Nymphæa (rubra) Spodeana.
Mrs Spode's Nymphæa.

63

Nymphaea devoniensis

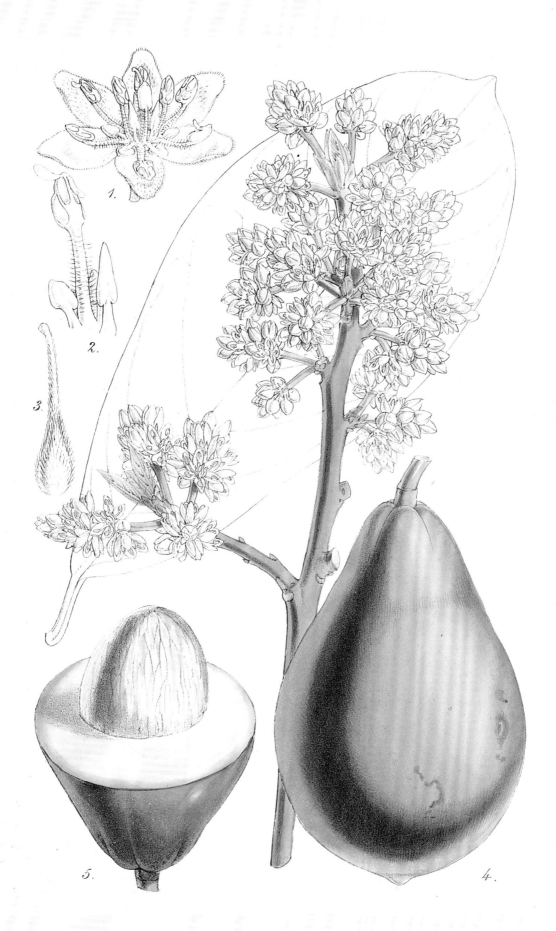

1.

2.

3.

5.

4.

64

Persea americana

W.H. Fitch, del.

Chromolith. Severeyns, Brussels.

65

Apple 'Yellow Bellefleur'

66

1 *Armillaria mellea;*   2 *Tricholoma equestre;*   3 *T. imbricatum;*   4 *T. sulphureum;*
5 *Calocybe gambosa;*   6 *T. album;*   7 *Lepista nuda*

67

Begonia tenera var. *thwaitesii*

PLATE IV

68

Victoria amazonica dissections

PLATE 1.

69

Victoria amazonica

PLATE II.

70

Victoria amazonica, opening flower

PLATE III

FRÉDÉRIC REEVE IMP.

W. FITCH. DEL. ET LITH

71

Victoria amazonica, expanded flower

72

Mango Mountain, from the summit of the Great Moraine in Yangma Valley, a watercolour
sketch by Fitch from one of Joseph Hooker's Indian field sketches

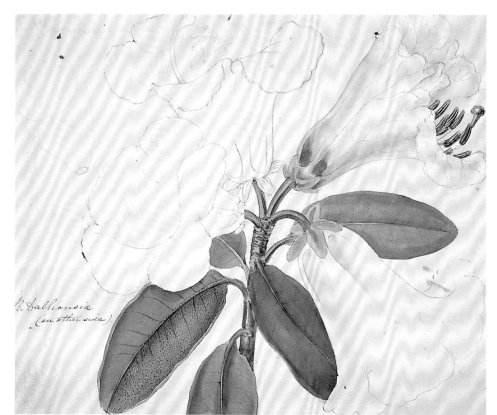

Three illustrations of *Rhododen-dron dalhousiae*, showing Fitch's working methods. Bottom left: field sketch by Joseph Dalton Hooker, showing how the plant grows on a tree. This was worked up by Fitch into the coloured plate shown bottom right. Top left: a detail of Fitch's drawing of the same plant, half-finished.